Getting through Dental Fear with CBT:
A young person's guide

By Helen Chapman and Nick Kirby-Turner

Series Editor: Dr Claudia Herbert

Contents

Introduction	03
What is dental fear	04
What causes fear and anxiety?	06
Getting through dental fear with CBT	12
What to expect from CBT	14
Getting through the feelings of fear	30
Ways of bypassing your fear	33
Preparing for the future	35
Finding a therapist	37
Finding a dentist	38
Further information	40
Epilogue	41
References	42
Further information	43
Index	44
Feedback form	47

Introduction

Everyone should visit the dentist. It is important to get your teeth checked for early decay that only the dentist can see. It also means that the dentist can teach you how to look after your teeth properly so that they last you for life.

Unfortunately anxiety about going to the dentist is quite common. Sometimes the fear can be so strong that you may want to avoid going to the dentist altogether. Alternatively, you may be terrified when you are at the dentist's. When a fear is that bad then it is called a phobia. In this case, because the fear is about visiting or receiving treatment from a dentist, it is called "dental phobia" or "dental fear". In this book, we shall call it dental fear.

As a young person, you may not be allowed to avoid visiting the dentist - your parents or carers may make you go. Some of you may even have been held down to have treatment when you were younger.

This book is aimed at helping young people with such strong dental fear that they need the help of a therapist to overcome the problem. Together with your therapist you can use the CBT techniques explained in this booklet and work with a sympathetic dentist to help you overcome your fear.

What is dental fear?

Dental fear shows up in your thoughts, feelings, bodily reactions and what you do. It can look like the list below. You may recognize some of the things on the list and there may be other things you would like to add to the list.

Thoughts
Before you go
It will hurt
The dentist will laugh at me
I will choke if the chair goes back
I need so much work doing
Other thoughts

"It will hurt"

"The dentist will laugh at me"

While you are there
It will hurt
I don't know what is happening
I can't stop the dentist
I don't like the dentist coming in close to me
I will choke if the chair goes back
Other thoughts

"I will choke if the chair goes back"

Feelings
Scared
Nervous
Worried
Terrified
Vulnerable
Other feelings

Body reactions

Heart beating faster
Breathing quickly
Tense muscles
Sweating
Feeling sick
Butterflies in the stomach
Wanting to go to the toilet
Everything looking bigger
than usual
Other bodily reactions

Things you might do (behaviours)

Avoiding going to the dentist
Gripping the arms of the dentist's chair
Holding the body tense ready for the pain
Screwing your eyes tightly shut so you can't see.
Other behaviours

Some people who are afraid of the dentist are actually afraid
of the sight of blood. This includes some people who are
scared of injections. These people faint at the dentist's rather
than becoming very tense. This problem refers to another
kind of fear, called 'blood' or 'needle' phobia. Strategies for
this are also covered in a separate book as part of this series.

What causes fear and anxiety?

Human beings in their natural state (without modern technology) are more vulnerable than many animals. The humans who first lived on this earth did not have much natural protection. Therefore, in order to survive as a species they needed to be able to respond quickly to danger. For example, an instant response to danger such as meeting a tiger in the jungle was essential to their survival. Humans have the ability to respond to situations of danger in three ways. The first response is the so-called 'fight' response. This might involve actual fight or

some other way of confronting the dangerous situation. If a fight response is not possible, the human organism is designed to try a 'flight' response. This would involve getting away or fleeing from the dangerous situation in some way. Only if fight or flight responses are not possible, a third response comes into action. This is known as the 'freeze' response. The freeze response is the most serious. This literally involves the human organism flopping into a state of complete numbness. When a person goes through a freeze response they feel externally really cold and numb, but internally they often feel really alert and in a lot of tension. The freeze response is there because it might just trick the source of danger. Have you ever seen a mouse 'playing dead' when it is caught by a cat? The cat often drops the mouse and leaves it alone. If the mouse is 'dead' when caught, the cat does not know how long it has been dead. It might have been dead a while and be 'off'. So, from the cat's point of view it is better to be safe than sorry and leave the mouse alone. The same applies to humans caught as lunch by that hungry tiger. The other advantage to a drop in blood pressure is that any wounds inflicted by the tiger do not bleed as badly and you are more likely to survive an attack.

When you are in a frightening situation, all of these three above responses are possible. Your body automatically produces a hormone called adrenalin or epinephrine. This hormone prepares your body to deal with the threat. It does this in a number of ways:

1. your heart beats faster and harder, sending more blood to your muscles so that you are geared up to run away, fast.

2. you breathe more quickly so that you are taking in more oxygen to supply the muscles.

3. blood supply to those parts of the body that are not necessary for running away, such as the stomach and the head, is reduced in order to save energy.

4. you may also become much more alert. It would be like focussing on the tiger, rather than taking your eyes off it. Noises may seem louder – good hearing would, for example, help you to detect a second tiger stalking you from behind.

5. you may sweat. Sweating helps to cool muscles that are working hard while you run away. It also makes you slippery, so, for example, the tiger may just loose his grip on you.

These changes in your body can give rise to a set of funny feelings, especially if you cannot fight or run away (flight) as in the case of a visit to the dentist. In this instance, you may experience yourself going into a freeze response, because of your fear. For example, you may notice the increase in heart rate as 'palpitations' or as skipped heartbeats. Breathing hard without using the extra oxygen can make you feel light-headed or dizzy, so can the slight reduction in blood supply to the head. The reduced blood supply to the stomach can give you feelings of 'butterflies' or make you feel sick.

These days, we rarely meet tigers in the jungle, but the fight-flight response is still useful. For example, if a car suddenly speeds around a corner while you are crossing a road, you run to get out of the way without having to think about it. Only after you have arrived safely on the pavement do you realise that your heart is thumping and you are breathing hard and feel scared.

Your adrenalin levels and your fear response decrease once you are away from the frightening situation. This happens gradually and will take a little while. It is shown in the graph below.

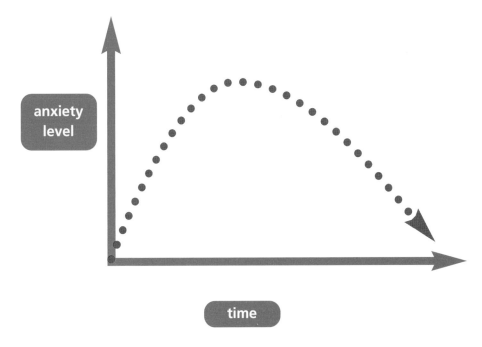

anxiety level

time

The feeling of fear can be so very unpleasant that you will do almost anything to reduce it. The most common thing is to try and escape from the situation, which is frightening, or just not to go there. However, while this is very understandable, it can cause problems. An example of this is a situation where there is no real danger and therefore there is nothing to be scared about, just as sitting in the dentist's chair, for example, is not dangerous. However, trying to escape and not stay on it means that you are signalling to your brain that this is dangerous. Therefore you fail to learn that just sitting in the chair is perfectly safe. However, if, despite feeling some initial fear, you were to stay in the dentist's chair, your adrenalin levels would drop and you would start to feel more comfortable. The next time you do it, you will feel less scared and less uncomfortable because you have taught yourself that your discomfort reduces as you stay in the situation.

In people who faint, something different happens. To start with they feel anxious and their heartbeat gets faster. Then, suddenly, their blood pressure drops, their heartbeat slows and they faint. This is part of the third response of our survival system, the freeze response, which was described, above.

The problem for many people about going to the dentist is that they have had a bad experience. Maybe in the past they have had experiences where it has hurt or felt very unpleasant. For them, the thing they worry about, such as being hurt, is a real possibility. It is important that you realise that today, almost 100% of dentistry can be completely pain free. If you are very, very, unlucky and it is not, then it is important that you know that you can sort out a way of letting the dentist know that you have a problem. Your dentist should understand this and should then help you some more.

Evidence from scientific studies suggests that for most people their worries are worse than what actually happens when they experience the feared situation. In other words if you can be brave enough to 'have a go', you are likely to find out that it was actually easier than you had previously thought. More about this later.

The good news is that using CBT with your therapist and a sympathetic dentist can help you overcome your fear. In the first instance it will be important that you find a dentist who will spend the time on using the approach described in this booklet to help you with your fear. Many dentists treat people who are scared by giving them tablets, happy gas or an injection in the arm to sedate them. The injection can make you feel dopy. It is not a general anaesthetic, which is rarely used for dental treatment these days. More on this later.

Getting through dental fear with CBT

CBT is based on the idea that what you feel and do is influenced by how you think.

Let's look at these examples

James and Peter are sitting in the dentist's waiting room, waiting to have a check up. James is thinking, "I don't know what is going to happen. The dentist will hurt me. I will choke when I lie down." James' thoughts make him feel scared and frightened of his check-up. He thinks that he is not going to be able to cope.

Peter is thinking, "It's just a check up; just the mirror and the air. If I don't understand what is going on, I can put up my hand, stop the dentist and ask a question." Peter's thoughts help him to prepare for the check up. They make him feel calm and he thinks he will be able to cope and feel in control.

When you think about this, who of the two is feeling more scared? Can you see that if you had James's thoughts, you would be likely to make yourself feel more scared, rather than less scared?

The above example therefore shows that thoughts really affect the way we feel. If your thoughts are coping or positive, like Peter's thoughts, they are less likely to make you feel frightened. However, if they are negative or make you think that you have no control, like James' thoughts, they are likely to make you feel scared. The types of thoughts that make you feel good and make you feel frightened are explained in more detail later.

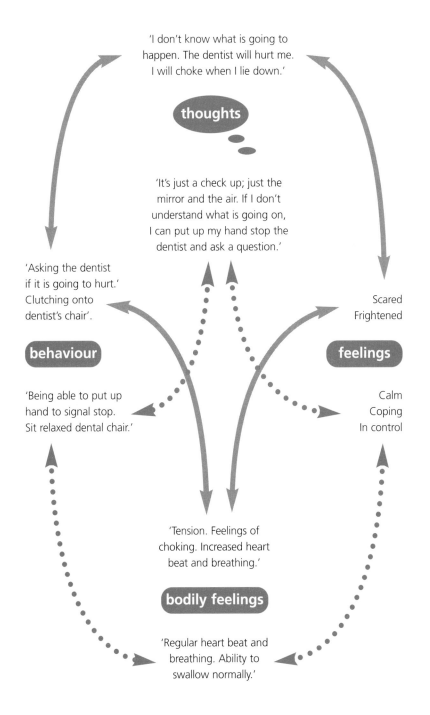

'I don't know what is going to happen. The dentist will hurt me. I will choke when I lie down.'

thoughts

'It's just a check up; just the mirror and the air. If I don't understand what is going on, I can put up my hand stop the dentist and ask a question.'

'Asking the dentist if it is going to hurt.' Clutching onto dentist's chair'.

behaviour

'Being able to put up hand to signal stop. Sit relaxed dental chair.'

Scared
Frightened

feelings

Calm
Coping
In control

'Tension. Feelings of choking. Increased heart beat and breathing.'

bodily feelings

'Regular heart beat and breathing. Ability to swallow normally.'

What to expect from CBT

You and your therapist will talk about why you have become scared of the dentist. For some people, this is simply because they have been told, or read about, someone else's experiences. These are often the experiences of a relative. For others, they may have had a bad experience at the dentist when they were younger. Although it may be difficult to remember what and when it exactly happened, you do need to tell your therapist about it, as it will help him or her understand what is driving your fear. Sometimes, if it really frightened you, you may find it difficult to express your past experiences into words. In that case, it will still be important to tell your therapist that you had bad experiences in the past, even if you can't actually put them into words to describe them. Where your therapist believes it is essential for you to identify what happened, it could be helpful if your CBT therapist were also skilled in methods, such as EMDR (Eye Movement Desensitization and Reprocessing). This could help you trace back the event that first made you feel frightened without having to put it into words.

Your dentist will probably also need to know what happened. If you think you will find it difficult to tell him, then you might find it easier to write it down and give this to him or her in advance.

You will need to talk to your therapist about what is keeping you feeling frightened and you will explore together how your thoughts, feelings and behaviours link up. Together you will draw up a map to help you understand your problems.

The therapist may also help explain your problems to the dentist. Although the therapist will have helped lots of people with problems, you are the expert on your problems. It is important that you find a way of communicating comfortably and confidently with your dentist as you will eventually be able to go to the dentist by yourself.

Overcoming your fear will involve:
1. spotting the thoughts that make you feel frightened.
2. learning to ask for the information that will allow you to question and change those thoughts.
3. learning to relax your body, or, if you faint, learning how not to faint.
4. gradually trying out and coping with different types of dental treatment, depending on the treatment you may need.

'Sort your thoughts'

We call thoughts, which make us feel frightened **'spiky thoughts'** because they are unhelpful. They 'spike' us by making us feel frightened and uncomfortable. We will call thoughts that make us feel better **'smooth thoughts'** because they are more helpful. They help us deal with situations and relax. A way to identify smooth thoughts is to imagine what a really good friend would be saying to you if they were in your head. One particularly good way is to think about how they would encourage and reward you both for your efforts and your successes.

When you are frightened, spiky thoughts are around, making you believe that something bad is bound to happen and that you will not be able to cope.

Catching spiky thoughts

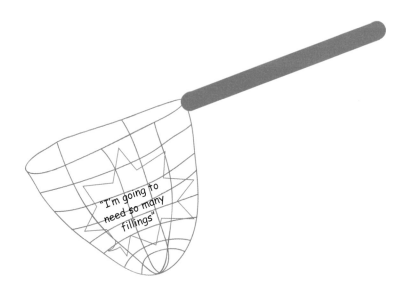

Sometimes your spiky thoughts are so much part of your visit to the dentist that you do not know they are there. Being able to spot the spiky thoughts is the first step to dealing with them. This can be difficult to start with. Once you've spotted the spiky thoughts, which are making you feel worse, you can work at developing smooth thoughts, which will help you feel better.

It helps to 'catch' your spiky thoughts and feelings by writing them down on a record. You may only have spiky thoughts about the dentist just before you go, but you may be able to find them by imaging that you are at the dentist. You may not feel terribly safe doing this on your own to start with, so you may need to start to do this when your therapist is around to help you feel safe.

For example:

Situation	Feeling	Spiky thought
Having a check up	Frightened/scared	I'm going to need so many fillings

Other things that make it easier to catch spiky thoughts are:

- Practice.
- Noticing if you suddenly feel worse (or better) – ask yourself what was going through your mind as, or just before, this happened.
- Noticing any pictures or images in your head when you felt worse or better.
- Asking yourself what you thought would happen.
- Asking yourself what you thought you could do about it.

Once you have learned how to catch the spiky thoughts you will be ready to question them so that they become less spiky, or even smooth.

Looking for evidence

Once you have caught a spiky thought, you need to question it carefully in order to change the way you feel. You may find there is a different way of looking at the situation.

1. Start by writing down all the reasons (evidence for), which you think support the spiky thought.

2. Get together all the evidence that you can think of against the spiky thought being true all the time. The following questions can help you with this:

The **'best mate'** question:
How would someone else I respect think about this situation?
What would they say to make me feel better?

The **'last time'** question:
What actually happened last time I was in this situation?

The **'what could I do'** question:
What could I actually do to deal with the situation?

The **'hard time'** question:
Am I giving myself a hard time?

The **'time travel'** question:
If I travelled in time three years ahead, how would I look at it?

The **'tunnel vision'** question:
Am I forgetting what I can do to deal with the situation?

diary can be downloaded from www.oxdev.co.uk

Situation	Feeling	Spiky thought	Evidence for	Evidence against	Weighing it all up
About to have a polish	Frightened	I will choke	Mum says she gags when she has it done. I won't be able to tell the dentist if I feel sick	The dentist says I'll be fine I didn't choke when I had my check up	I may not be the same as Mum. I'll tell the dentist what I'm worried about Perhaps he will let me stop him
About to have a filling	Very frightened	It will hurt	It really did hurt last time	I've got a new dentist who seems really nice She says she's going to make the tooth go numb. She's given me a signal to tell her to stop.	Most people have fillings without it hurting If it hurts I can use the stop signal and tell her

3. Weighing it up.
   After you have collected all the
   evidence it is time to weigh up the
   evidence for and against the spiky
   thought. This will help you question
   your thought – is it really all that spiky?

Some of these questions might help you with weighing the
evidence against the spiky thoughts:

- Do I know this is going to happen for a fact, or is it just
  something I've heard or read about?
- Is there anything different about this time and previous
  visits?
- What has the dentist told me about what is going to
  happen?
- What has the dentist told me to do if my spiky thought
  comes true?
- What do I need to ask the dentist so that I can fill in this
  column?

Testing it out

Some of your spiky thoughts may be founded on genuine,
but unfortunate experiences. It is therefore important that you
and your therapist talk to your dentist about the safe ways
you can test out your spiky thoughts. If you test out your
spiky thoughts in this way, you will be able to find out if your
worst predictions and fears come true every time you go to
the dentist.

There are 4 steps to follow:

1. The prediction:

   Write down what you think will happen in the situation. This includes what you believe will happen, how the dentist and other people in the surgery will behave and what you might do. The sort of things you might do should include what you would have done before you started this treatment and also the sorts of things you could do now that might be helpful. These helpful things are called "coping strategies." There are some examples of these in the next section.

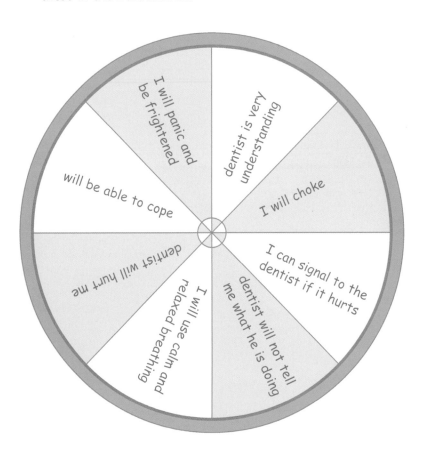

2. The test:

   This will have to be negotiated with the dentist. There is a companion book to this one, titled: "Getting through Dental Fear with CBT – A Resource Book for Dentists and Therapists", which will give you, your therapist or your dentist some ideas of what to choose for such a test. It will be important to start with something that does not feel too scary for you to test at first. Gradually, as you feel more comfortable, you can increase the level of difficulty. The fear ladder, below, will also help you with this.

3. The results:

   What actually happened? Did the predictions that you initially made come true?

4. Conclusions:

   What does your experience tell you about the spiky thoughts?

Here is an example:

Ali does not want to go for a check up. His spiky thoughts are telling him that he is frightened and does not want to go.

1. Prediction:

   Ali's beliefs about what is going to happen are, *"The dentist will not tell me what he is going to do. I will choke when the chair goes flat."*

2. The test:

   Ali plans to go to the dentist and to ask him to tell him before he does anything. He wants to ask the dentist to only put the chair back a little way.

3. Results:

   After the test, Ali describes what happened. "It was really hard, but I plucked up enough courage to ask the dentist to tell me before he did anything. He looked a little surprised, but he did it. When it came to putting the chair back, he suggested that I said 'Ready, steady, go!', to tell him when to start, and to say "Stop" when I was beginning to feel uncomfortable.

4. Conclusions:

   Ali concluded: "I asked the dentist to tell me what was happening and he did it. It felt much better to know what was going on. I will remind him that I like to be told what is happening when I go next time. I'm sure he won't mind. It was a good idea to be able to tell the dentist when to start moving the chair. I'll ask if I can do that next time as well. I didn't let the chair go back very far, but the dentist said I'd manage it further next time. I think he might be right, though I don't think it will be very much extra".

These four steps should form a cycle – once you've reached a set of conclusions, you can decide on the next test to carry out.

For example, Ali's next test could be: "I will not choke if the dentist puts the chair half way back. But I know that if I feel uncomfortable before that I can say and he will stop. The important thing is to get it further back than last time."

The fear ladder

When you are scared of the dentist, there are usually some things that you fear more than others. It can be useful to write these down. They can then be ordered up a fear ladder (or hierarchy). The top rung of the ladder is the thing you fear most, for example, having a filling. The other rungs up the ladder are other easier things, such as check ups and polishing which might not scare you as much. Your therapist may ask you to complete one of these. Doing this will help you, your therapist and your dentist decide the order in which to introduce different types of treatment to you. You will usually work up the ladder rung by rung. If the gap between two rungs is too big to manage as one step, you can put in as many extra little rungs as you need.

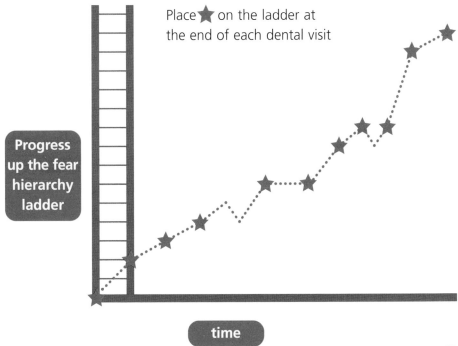

Place ⭐ on the ladder at the end of each dental visit

Progress up the fear hierarchy ladder

time

Let's think about an example:

Nadia is fine about having check ups and polishing, but is terrified of fillings. She manages a complete check up at her first visit and has a polish at her second visit. She is not frightened during either of these. By this time she is confident that her dentist will explain everything and stop when she requests. She therefore decides to try to have a filling at the next visit. To help her get used to the drills before she has a proper filling, Nadia and her dentist first spend some extra time introducing her to the noise and the feel of the drills. When Nadia feels comfortable with this, she decides to ask the dentist to go ahead with the filling.

Compared to Nadia, Ali does not feel comfortable about check-ups, yet. You can see that it is going to take Ali several visits to be able to accept a check up with the chair fully flat, as the dentist would usually like it in order to be able to see the teeth properly.

How long does each step take? This will vary between people. For some, each step may only take a few minutes, for others, it could take longer, sometimes even several visits. It is important to remember the anxiety graph. It may be that once you realise that your spiky thoughts were unrealistic, your fear level will drop very rapidly. On the other hand, it may be that the dentist needs to make a short item take a long time, or that you need to practice over and over again, so that your fear levels can drop before you go on to the next rung on your ladder.

Pat yourself on the back

It is really important that you recognise your own progress. Smooth thoughts should include telling yourself when you are doing well. It is important that you believe you can succeed. This may be difficult at first, but it should get easier for you the more progress you make.

It is also great if, for each rung or small step up the ladder, you (or your parents) give you a reward to help you celebrate your success. This can be something quite small, like a magazine or music token. Or it could be a family event like a trip out for the day. You need to agree what this will be beforehand and remember that your parents or carers must be able to afford it!

Traps for the unwary

It is common to have some setbacks. As you try out new things related to your fear, they will not always work. There are a number of common traps that people fall into when trying to overcome their dental fear. These are now listed, below:

1. You may be very hard on yourself. When you are away from the dentist's, you may tell yourself that you are stupid for being so scared of something that should be so easy and that you should be able to do better. You will do better next time! Don't bully yourself like this. Part of the definition of a phobia is that it seems to be quite an irrational fear. (Often the fear is more severe than may make sense to you). Therefore feeling like this is normal for some people and it is important that you treat yourself kindly.

2. You may expect yourself to do too much at once. You then fail. Don't push yourself into trying to climb the fear ladder faster than you can manage comfortably. Every time that you over-reach yourself and slip down or off the ladder, it becomes more difficult to get back on and climb up it again. Slow and steady does the trick. Your rate of climbing is likely to increase as treatment goes on. Therefore, allow yourself to be patient – be kind and give yourself a chance. If you do slip down or fall off the ladder, your dentist and/or therapist will help you get back on. Often this will be a little lower down, at a place you will feel comfortable with and from which you can climb up again.

3. Parents (and sometimes dentists) ask you to do too much in one go. Often this is just because they want you to get better quickly. However, sometimes parents may ask you to do too much too soon because they resent the amount of time they are spending with you at the dentist. It is important that you tell your therapist and dentist that this is happening and explore the support they can give you in explaining your needs to your parents. Often, this is because your parents may not quite understand how scary your fear can feel. They may also feel quite helpless because they don't know how to make you feel better.

Coping skills or behaviours

Learning to question the spiky thoughts is one set of skills you may already be quite good at by now.

Also, the sorts of things you do when you are at the dentist will affect how tense or frightened you will feel.

First, let's do a small experiment:

While you're sitting here, put the book down and clench your hands into fists. Notice exactly what is happening to you. Does the rest of you feel tense as well? Did you stop breathing for a few seconds? Was there anything else that you noticed you did that suggests that you tensed up?

Can you see, based on the experiment, that if you are tense, for example, holding tight to the arms of the dentist's chair, the rest of you might feel tense as well? That will have two effects:

- It will make it harder for the dentist to work. If your cheeks are tense and stiff while he or she tries to pull them out of the way to see, he or she will have to pull harder and it may become uncomfortable for you.
- It might well make you feel more scared because the tension in your muscles is similar to that which you get when you are scared.

So, if you are tense, it is harder to have treatment. If you are finding it uncomfortable to have treatment, then your spiky thoughts may come back. This is then part of a vicious circle of things getting worse. However, there is something that you can do to work against this – relax! If you can relax your muscles, you'll reverse the circle. If you find it difficult to relax your muscles when you tell them to there are many techniques that you can learn that make this easier for you. Your therapist can teach you how to do this (see later).

There are other things you can do to improve the way things go for you. You can make sure that you have negotiated a stop signal with the dentist. This is usually putting up a hand or any similar signal that you agree with your dentist beforehand. Some dentists will stop automatically if you do this. However, they might forget to tell you that you can do this and therefore it is much better to check out which signal to use with your dentist before you start on any of your treatments.

Something, which your therapist will know about, but your dentist may not, is a fear scale or a fear thermometer. Here, you have a scale of between 0 and 10, where 0 means 'not frightened at all' and 10 means that this is 'the most frightened you could be.' When you are trying out new types of treatment, you can use this to let the dentist know how scared you are. You should notice the number on your scale or thermometer drop as you get used to, and more comfortable with, doing the new things. There are other ideas that could be helpful to you in the resource book for your therapist and dentist.

Getting through the feelings of fear

Your therapist may decide that it would be a good idea to teach you how to relax while you are at the dentist. Relaxation can help you at the dentist's in two ways. First, it will make your muscles, including those in your mouth, floppier. Relaxed, floppy muscles mean that your cheeks and tongue are easier for the dentist and nurse to hold out of the way, gently, so that they can see what they are doing. Therefore, you are less likely to feel discomfort during dental procedures. Secondly, relaxation helps you to feel confident about dealing with spiky thoughts. You are more likely to notice any spiky thoughts and feel more positive about doing something about them. Generally, relaxation makes you feel good as it helps your whole body to be more at ease.

There are three main ways you can relax. Your therapist may choose one or a combination of any of these to help you relax.

Controlled Breathing

This helps you control the rapid breathing that goes with fear. When you learn to breathe more slowly, deeply and regularly into the bottom of your stomach, you will be able to feel calmer.

Using your Imagination

You can leave your spiky thoughts behind you by going to a relaxing place in your imagination. This could, for example, be a beach or somewhere else that feels really good to you; it may be a place that you have been to on holiday. It could also be a favourite activity such as going to a fair. You can use almost any situation, in which you feel confident, safe and relaxed. Your therapist can help you to develop such a safe place.

Muscle Relaxation

This can be as simple as just learning to let your muscles go floppy, one after the other, or it can be slightly more complicated – in which case it is called progressive muscle relaxation. Progressive muscle relaxation is used if you find it difficult to just let your muscles go floppy. Your therapist will be able to teach you how to tense your muscles before letting them relax.

The more you practice these exercises, the better you will get at them. In this way you will be really good at them when you need to use them to have treatment at the dentist.

If you are one of the people who faint at the dentist, you will not be taught these exercises as they drop your blood pressure and make you a bit more likely to faint. Instead you will be taught how to tense your legs and maybe your stomach to help you not to faint. Again, your therapist will be able to teach you the right methods for this.

Mindfulness

Sometimes your therapist will teach you ways of enhancing both the thinking skills and relaxing skill you have already learned. This is known as mindfulness. It helps you to pay attention to what is going on in your body, your emotions and your thoughts and to notice these in a different way. By accepting them rather than fighting them, you can then relate to thoughts and feelings for what they are rather than attending to all the baggage they bring with them. You learn the skills of detaching yourself from past unhelpful memories, almost as if you were seeing them for the first time. Rather than distracting yourself, you learn to tune in to the here-and-now. When you are able to do this you discover that thoughts and feelings are just that – thoughts and feelings. They are temporary. They fade with time and are no more fact or real than any other thought or feeling. Mindfulness can help free you from the tyranny of fear.

Ways of bypassing your fear

Your dentist may suggest other ways of helping you have dental treatment. These rely on drugs to dull your fear by sedating you or making you feel dopey and forgetful, so that you are less aware of what is happening and remember less about what happened. Some people find that they can gradually wean themselves from the need to have sedation, but others find they cannot give it up.

There are three types of sedation:

1. Diazepam or Valium tablets. These are rarely used for young people as their results can be unreliable in some people. You may also come to rely on them rather than facing your fear.

2. Relative Analgesia, which is also known as inhalational sedation and happy gas. This is a common type of sedation. You breathe the gas through a mask that just fits over your nose. The dentist gives you just enough gas to make you feel warm and floaty. Your dentist, or your therapist, may also help you to have a daydream while you are breathing the gas.

3. Intravenous sedation (Midozalam) – this is administered through an injection in the arm. You are more likely to be offered this form of sedation if you are older. If this is used, you will be quite heavily sedated (sleepy) and will remember very little about the treatment.

Whatever type of sedation you have, you will need to be accompanied to the dentist and afterwards by an adult. You should not do things like riding a bike or doing gymnastics for 24 hours afterwards.

You may be offered a general anaesthetic (GA) to have dental treatment. When this is used, you go completely to sleep as you would for an operation. It is carried out in a hospital. It is used very rarely these days and usually only if you need to have very difficult or urgent dental treatment.

Our feeling is that you are better off working through your fear with the CBT methods suggested here and the help of a therapist. This should give you the confidence and the skills to have dental treatment in the normal way for the rest of your life. But, if you have very large amounts of difficult or urgent dental treatment to do, it might be sensible to have just the difficult or urgent stuff (or perhaps all of it) done under sedation or general anaesthetic if your dentist suggests it. Then, when you are finished, you can start with CBT. This means that when you need your next treatment, you are all ready to have it without sedation. You need to discuss the reasons for the dentist offering you sedation or anaesthesia carefully with the dentist and your therapist. It is helpful for you to remember that the sedation or general anaesthetic would only be a short-term solution, but will usually not help you to overcome and master your dental fear. CBT would be more effective at this.

Preparing for the future

Once you've found a dentist whom you trust and you've started to climb your ladder successfully, you may find you get to the top without stopping. Some people find that they have a setback and need to go back down a rung or two on the ladder. It is then possible to reclimb the steps, but perhaps in slightly smaller increments. This is fairly common. If you have to do this it gives you even more opportunity to practice your new skills. Therefore don't worry about this. It gives you a good chance to really master those steps at a pace that is comfortable for you.

For many people, these setbacks happen in the long gaps between completing one course of dental treatment and starting another. It might therefore be sensible to keep these gaps short to start with and gradually make them longer. Whatever happens, it is really important that once you have overcome your fear and had all the treatment you need that you keep going to the dentist regularly. There are two reasons for this:

- Attending regularly allows the dentist to find new cavities (decay) when they are small. They are then quick and easy to fix. It also allows him or her to do preventive treatments such as fissure sealants and showing you any places you are not cleaning properly. In this way, you can help to keep your teeth really healthy and reduce the need for actual dental treatment.

- Going regularly and having any type of treatment you need is the best way of staying fear-free. This is because each time you see the dentist, it gives you another opportunity to practice and to learn to feel comfortable with these visits.

Finding a therapist

Your General Practitioner (GP) should direct you towards local services where therapy is available free as part of the NHS. There are also organizations that offer CBT on a private basis, in which case therapy would need to be paid for. You have the right to ask about your therapist's qualifications, change therapists if you are unhappy and to check that your therapist is registered with a professional organization, such as the British Psychological Society (BPS).

With CBT, the overall monitoring and accreditation organization is the British Association of Behavioural and Cognitive Psychotherapies (BABCP). The address for the BABCP is:

BABCP
The Globe Centre
PO Box 9
Accrington
BB5 OXB

info@babcp.com
Tel   01254 875 277
Fax 01254 239 114

If you are looking for a CBT therapist, who is additionally qualified in the use of EMDR (Eye Movement Desensitization and Reprocessing), you must check that they are properly trained to either Practitioner or Consultant level. You can check therapist's accreditations, by visiting the following website:

www.emdr-uki.org

Finding a dentist

There are several ways to find a sympathetic dentist.

- Ask your family and friends if they go to a dentist they think will be sympathetic and understanding.

- Ask your local Primary Care Trust (PCT) for the name and phone number of the Dental Services Manager of your local Community Dental Service (CDS) or Personal Dental Service (PDS). You may find that these dentists seem to be a little less rushed and have more time to help you. The Dental Services Manager may be able to suggest a dentist who is particularly interested in helping patients who are frightened. The manager may also have a copy of the British Society for the Behavioural Sciences in Dentistry (BSBSD) Directory, 2000. This book was sent to all Health Authorities when it was first published, but may no longer be available. It listed the names of dentists who used behavioural methods (part of CBT) to treat patients who are dentally fearful.

- Use websites. Some are listed below.
www.bda-findadentist.org.uk
  – (to find a dentist)

  www.beyondfear.org
  – Links to dentists (General Dental Practitioners or GDPs) treating anxious patients, largely by sedation

  www.dentalhealth.org.uk
  - British Dental Health Foundation (helpline 0870 770 4000)

In whatever way you find your dentist, it could be helpful to ask the dental receptionist some questions such as
- How many fearful patients does the dentist treat?
- Does the dentist give patients a stop signal?
- What does the dentist do if you say that treatment is painful?
- Will the dentist be able to offer you treatment on the NHS, or will it be private?

If the receptionist does not know the answers to these questions, ask the dentist to ring you back for a chat and ask him or her directly.

Further information

If you have difficulty finding CBT treatment for your dental fear and you don't want to have sedation or a general anaesthetic, there are two other treatments, which some dentists use to help their frightened patients. The most popular is hypnosis. This type of hypnosis is not the same as the 'showtime' hypnosis you see on TV programmes. The other is neuro-linguistic programming, which is not so widely available.

- www.healthyteeth.com
  – Dental Anxiety and Phobia Association (run by a dentist with training in hypnosis)
- www.bsmdh.com
  – British Society of Medical & Dental Hypnosis
  (0700 0560 309)

Epilogue

Congratulations! Now you have got to this part of the booklet, you have found out that you can do something very positive to master your dental fear. You may already have found yourself a CBT therapist or you may still be in the process of organizing this for yourself. We wish you every success with tackling your dental fear and hope that this booklet will prove a useful guide.

References

Chapman, HR & Kirby-Turner, NC (1999) - Dental fear in children – A proposed model. British Dental Journal: 187(3); 408-12

Chapman, HR & Kirby-Turner, NC (2002) – Visual/verbal analogue scales: examples of brief assessment methods to aid management of child and adult patients in clinical practice. British Dental Journal: 193(8); 447-50

Chapman, HR & Kirby-Turner, NC. (2005) – The treatment of dental fear in children and adolescents-- a cognitive-behavioural approach to the development of coping skills and their clinical application. In New Research on the Psychology of Fear Paul L. Gower (ed) Nova Publishers Inc, Hauppauge, New York

Further information

'So young, so sad, so listen'
By Philip Graham & Carol Hughes
Available from the Royal College of Psychiatrists
Tel 020 7235 2351

www.youngminds.org.uk
An organization for young people, their parents and
professionals concerned about young people's mental health.

www.bullying.co.uk
For people who have been bullied

www.childline.org.uk
For children in trouble or danger
Tel 0800 1111

www.samaritans.org.uk
Samaritans: 08457 909090
jo@samaritans.org

Parents' Information Service
0800 018 2138

Index

Adrenalin 03, 06, 08, 09, 10, 24, 40
Anxiety 06, 24, 40
    Anxiety curve 09
Behaviour 05, 13
    Avoidance 05
    Coping – see coping skills 20
Behavioural experiments 20, 23, 28
Body reactions - also see bodily feelings 04, 13
Bypassing fear - see general anaesthetic and sedation 33
Cognitive Behavioural Therapy (CBT) 03, 11, 12, 14, 21, 34, 37, 38, 40, 41
How thoughts, feelings and behaviours link up 13
What to expect from CBT 14
Coping skills or behaviours 05, 13, 20
Dental fear 03, 04, 12, 21, 26, 34, 40, 41, 42
Dental phobia 03
Dental Treatment 11, 15, 33, 34, 35, 36
Benefits
    Short-term or long-term 34
    Telling the dentist about what has happened in the past 14
    Telling the dentist that something is wrong 29
    Questions to ask at the dentist 39
    See also stop signal 29
EMDR (Eye movement desensitisation
    and reprocessing) 14, 37
Fainting 09
Fear ladder or hierarchy 21, 23, 27
Fear thermometer 29
Feelings (see also Getting through the feelings) 04, 08, 09, 14, 16, 30, 32

Fight, flight or freeze response 08, 09
Finding a dentist 38
Finding a therapist 37
Further information 40, 43
General Anaesthetic (GA) 11, 34, 40
Getting through the feelings of fear 30
Hypnosis 40
Mindfulness 32
Neuro-linguistic programming 40
Pain 11
Preparing for the future 35
Rate of progress 27
    Bullying 43
Relaxation 30
    Controlled breathing 30
    Imaginal relaxation 11
    Muscle relaxation 31
Reward (pat yourself on the back) 15, 25
Sedation 33
    Inhalational/relative analgesia(RA)/Happy Gas 33
    Intravenous (Midozalam) 34
    Oral (Valium) 33
Sort your thoughts 15
Stop signals 29
Testing it out 19
Thoughts
    Catching spiky thoughts 16
    Diary 18
    Looking for the evidence 17
    Questions to ask yourself 18, 19
    Smooth thoughts 15, 16, 25
Spiky thoughts 15, 16, 17, 19, 21, 24, 28, 30, 31

Testing it out 19
Weighing it up 19
Traps for the unwary 26
Understanding your problem 06
Websites 18, 37, 39, 40, 43

Can you help us please?

This is a short questionnaire to help us find out what kind of people read this book, and more importantly, which parts were helpful and which were not so helpful.

Please answer the questions as best you can and return the form to: Blue Stallion Publications, 8a Market Square, Witney, OX28 6BB by post, or complete the online questionnaire at: www.oxdev.co.uk

We assure you that we will deal strictly confidentially with all given information. That means that we would never release any personal information to a third party. We will only use the information to evaluate and improve the books.

How old are you? ☐ years
Are you male or female?   Male ☐   Female ☐
Who do you live with?   Mum ☐   Dad ☐
   Brothers, how many   ☐
   Sisters, how many   ☐
   Grandparents   ☐
   Other   ☐

What made you read the book?

Who recommended this book to you?

Who did you read it with?
By yourself   ☐
With a parent(s)   ☐
With a doctor/therapist   ☐
With someone else   ☐

Have you ever been to see a therapist/psychologist to help with your
difficulties?   Yes ☐   No ☐

Did the book make therapy any easier for you?
                                Yes ☐   No ☐
                  No difference ☐

How helpful have you found this book?
Please mark on the scale below.

1	2	3	4	5
Not at all helpful	Not that helpful	Quite helpful	Very helpful	Extremely Helpful

Did you find it easy to understand?

1	2	3	4	5
Extremely easy to understand	Mostly easy to understand	Some easy parts, some difficult to understand	Quite difficult to understand	Very difficult to understand

What was the most helpful thing you learned from this book?

Was there anything you didn't like about the book?

Would you recommend this book to someone else who had
difficulties?   Yes   No

Please add anything else that you think might be helpful for us to know.

Thank you for your information!

The Publisher